# FIRE SAFETY

 BOY SCOUTS OF AMERICA®

# Requirements

1. Do the following:
    a. Demonstrate the technique of stop, drop, roll, and cool. Explain how burn injuries can be prevented.
    b. List the most frequent causes of burn injuries.

2. Explain the chemistry and physics of fire. Name the parts of the fire tetrahedron. Explain why vapors are important to the burning process. Name the products of combustion. Give an example of how fire grows and what happens.

3. Name the most frequent causes of fire in the home, and give examples of ways they can be prevented. Include a discussion about fires caused by smoking in the home, cooking, candles, fireplaces, and electrical appliances.

4. Do the following:
    a. Explain the role of human behavior in the arson problem in this country.
    b. List the actions that cause seasonal fires and explain how these fires can be prevented.

5. List the common circumstances that cause holiday-related fires and explain how these fires can be prevented.

6. Conduct a home safety survey with the help of an adult. Then do the following:
    a. Draw a home fire-escape plan, create a home fire-drill schedule, and conduct a home fire drill.
    b. Test a smoke alarm and demonstrate regular maintenance of a smoke alarm.
    c. Explain what to do when you smell gas and when you smell smoke.

35896
ISBN 978-0-8395-3318-4
©2004 Boy Scouts of America
2011 Printing of the 2009 Revision

BANG/Brainerd, MN
6-2011/06214

d. Explain how you would report a fire alarm.

e. Explain what fire safety equipment can be found in public buildings.

f. Explain who should use fire extinguishers and when these devices can be used.

g. Explain how to extinguish a grease pan fire.

h. Explain what fire safety precautions you should take when you are in a public building.

7. Do the following:

a. Demonstrate lighting a match safely.

b. Demonstrate the safe way to start a charcoal fire.

c. Demonstrate the safe way to melt wax.

8. Explain the difference between combustible and noncombustible liquids and between combustible and noncombustible fabrics.

9. Do the following:

a. Demonstrate the safe way to fuel a lawn mower.

b. Demonstrate the safety factors, such as proper ventilation, for auxiliary heating devices and the proper way to fuel those devices.

10. Do the following:

a. Explain the cost of outdoor and wildland fires and how to prevent them.

b. Demonstrate setting up and putting out a cooking fire.

c. Demonstrate using a camp stove and lantern.

d. Explain how to set up a campsite safe from fire.

11. Visit a fire station. Identify the types of fire trucks. Find out about the fire prevention activities in your community.

12. Choose a fire safety–related career that interests you and describe the level of education required and responsibilities of a person in that position. Tell why this position interests you.

# Contents

# Introduction

The ability to use fire safely is essential to human survival. Fire is a part of life. By learning the skills described in this merit badge pamphlet, you will be better prepared to use fire safely.

This merit badge pamphlet will provide you with information on the science of fire, how to prevent home fires, and how to handle fire safely. There are also chapters on burn prevention, outdoor and camping safety, and your local fire service.

The goal of this merit badge pamphlet is to help you develop the knowledge and the skills necessary to prevent and to survive fires and burns.

## The Chemistry and Physics of Fire

Fire is a chemical reaction between oxygen and vapors known as *volatiles*. When the oxygen and vapors interact, two types of energies—heat and light—are given off in the form of flames. So when you see a burning log, the flames are not eating the wood; they are just a visible sign of fast *oxidation* (interaction of oxygen and another substance) known as *combustion*.

What causes something to give off volatile vapors? Usually, the answer is *heat*. When a substance is heated to a certain temperature, it gives off combustible vapors. Some substances require a lot of heat to give off these vapors, while others give off combustible vapors at room temperature or colder. It all depends on the substance and its condition. For instance, kindling, or small sticks of wood, catches fire more quickly than a big log. Both are made of the same material—wood—but because the sticks have more surface area exposed to oxygen, they are more easily combustible. So, vapors are important to the burning process because it is the vapors that are burning.

You may be wondering why a log turns into a pile of ashes if it is not being eaten by the flames—if the flames are just visible signs of the combustion taking place. Well, when the wood gives off combustible vapors, the chemistry of the wood changes and the wood *decomposes* (breaks down) until it is mostly just carbon—a simple element that all living things have in common.

If you are having trouble picturing this concept, imagine a s'more. If you take away the marshmallow, and then the chocolate, you no longer have a s'more. You only have graham crackers. When materials send vapors up and out, they change into a simpler thing.

# What Is Combustible?

Any substance that ignites or burns easily is said to be *combustible.* Examples are things like gasoline, paint thinner, and aerosols. Fire warnings are usually on the containers to warn consumers that such substances should be treated carefully. Things that are *noncombustible* are not as easily ignited; that is, they are not as likely to catch fire under normal conditions.

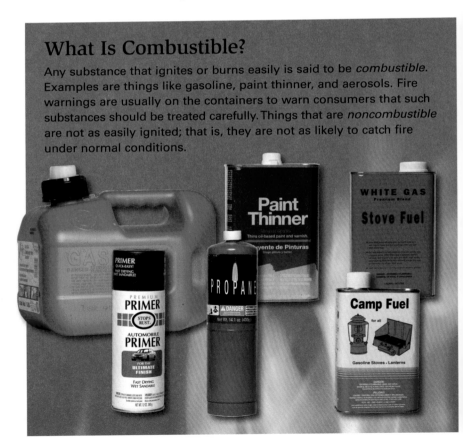

## The Fire Tetrahedron

For a fire to occur, four factors must be present: fuel, oxygen, heat, and a continuous chemical chain reaction. These four elements are known as the *fire tetrahedron*. A tetrahedron (pronounced *te'-truh-hee'-drohn*) is a solid shape with four *(tetra)* triangular faces *(hedron)*.

Simply put, firefighting and fire prevention are attempts to remove one or more elements of the fire tetrahedron. For instance, when you pour water on a campfire, you are removing heat. When you slide a lid on a pan fire, you are cutting off the supply of oxygen. When you keep newspapers away from a stove, you are separating fuel from a heat source.

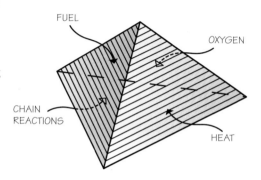

The four elements of the fire tetrahedron are:

**Fuel.** Anything that will produce combustible vapors qualifies as fuel. There are solid fuels (like wood), liquid fuels (like gasoline), and gaseous fuels (like methane).

**Oxygen.** An oxidizing agent is needed for the chemistry of fire. Most often, oxygen is that agent. The air we breathe, which is 21 percent oxygen, is usually enough to provide this piece of the fire tetrahedron.

**Heat.** When a substance is at a temperature sufficient for it to produce combustible vapors, all it takes to start a fire is the heat from an *ignition source,* such as the flame from a match.

**Unbroken chemical chain reaction.** This is the uninterrupted interaction of the heat, fuel, and oxygen that allows the fire to continue to burn. For instance, once you have lit a candle's wick, the heat from the candle's flame continues to melt the wax. The melted wax releases combustible vapors. Those new vapors mix with the oxygen in the air, creating more heat, which melts more wax, which gives off more combustible vapors.

## Products of Combustion

When a fire burns, it produces light, heat, gases, and particles, all of which affect humans in specific ways.

**Heat.** Your skin will start to burn at around 115 to 177 degrees. If you inhale air at this temperature, it will damage your lungs. Because the temperature in a house fire can reach approximately 2,000 degrees in less than 10 minutes, it is easy to understand why many people caught in house fires suffer inhalation burns.

**Gas.** The most common harmful gas produced by a fire is *carbon monoxide,* which is odorless, colorless, and tasteless. When you breathe in carbon monoxide, you become disoriented and sleepy, and you may fall unconscious and die. Carbon monoxide detectors can be purchased for your home and are especially helpful if your heating sources—like propane or natural gas heaters—use open flames.

**Particles.** The particles produced in a fire are called *soot.* Soot is mostly carbon particles of incompletely burned fuel. These particles combine with the gasses of the fire and make *smoke.* The particles in the air irritate your eyes, make you cough, and block your vision.

## Fire Dynamics

If paper is burning in a metal wastepaper basket in the middle of an empty parking lot, the danger of fire damage is small. The heat, gases, and particles will rise and scatter through the air. Eventually, all of the fuel in the basket will burn up and the fire will go out.

However, if the wastepaper basket is in your living room, the danger increases dramatically. Embers from the wastepaper basket may pop or float over to the couch and set it on fire. Then, the heat, gases, and particles can rise up, hit the ceiling, and spread. The heat and smoke will travel and set other fuels on fire—like plaster, electrical wires, plastics, and curtains. Large amounts of dangerous gases will be produced and fill the entire house in a matter of minutes, damaging property and killing or injuring the people and animals in the house. This chain of events is called *fire dynamics.*

# Preventing Fires

To prevent fires, you need to know what causes them. Most fires occur outside the home, but most deaths and injuries, and the greatest dollar loss, occur in residential fires. Individuals can have the biggest impact preventing residential fires.

## Sources of Fire

Fires can be started almost anywhere with almost any materials. The key to fire safety is knowing what types of materials and conditions are most susceptible to fire, then practicing safety precautions to minimize the chances of fire.

### Smoking

Cigarettes and matches, whether they are burning or merely smoldering, are sources of ignition and can easily set things like furniture and papers on fire. Fires caused by smoking can be avoided easily.

- The best way to keep cigarettes and pipes from starting a fire in your home is to have no smoking in your home. However, if someone does smoke where you live, be sure the smoker uses an ashtray.

- People should never smoke while sleepy, while in bed, or when drinking alcohol or taking medication, as they might be more careless in their handling of a lit cigarette.

- Cigarette butts should be cool before they are discarded, and ashtrays should be emptied into containers that will not catch fire, like a metal trash can.

In the United States, a fire department responds to a fire every 18 seconds. In the year 2001, excluding the events of September 11, there were 1.7 million fires. Property loss was estimated at $10.6 billion. A reported 3,745 people died. Of the 20,300 people who were injured, more than 75 percent were injured in residential fires.

## Furnaces

While the thermometer drops in the winter months, the chance of a furnace fire rises. Following a few precautions can help lower the probability of this type of fire.

• Keep a 3-foot area around the furnace clear of anything that could catch fire.

• Change the furnace filter regularly.

• Have the furnace professionally inspected as recommended by the manufacturer or at least once a year at the beginning of the heating season.

## Space Heaters

Space heaters usually are electric, but some burn fuel like propane, natural gas, or kerosene. While they are a convenient way to generate a great deal of heat in a small area, space heaters can be dangerous if certain safety measures are not followed.

• Keep a 3-foot area around and above the space heater clear of anything that could catch fire.

• Keep children away from the space heater, and make sure there is adult supervision in the room at all times the heater is turned on.

• Use a space heater only as a supplemental heat source.

• Make sure the wires of an electric heater are not frayed and that the outlet you use is grounded and not overloaded.

• Have wood burners and other solid-fuel devices inspected at least once a year.

• Use the correct fuel, and fuel the heater outside.

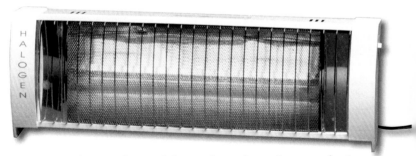

**Read and follow the manufacturer's instructions when using space heaters.**

## Fireplaces

Sitting in front of a roaring fireplace can be one of the joys of winter, but following a few safety rules can help keep the fire in its place.

- Always put a screen in front of the fireplace to keep embers from escaping and igniting materials like rugs or clothing.

- Keep things that could catch fire at least 3 feet away from the fireplace.

- Make sure children do not get too near the fireplace.

- Take ashes out and away from the house for proper disposal.

- Have the fireplace and chimney professionally cleaned and inspected at least once a year.

- Do not burn pressure-treated wood, shiny or metallic paper, or plastics in a fireplace or furnace. They give off toxic gasses.

- Do not burn green wood in a fireplace. It gives off too much smoke, burns unpredictably, and causes heavy creosote buildup, which is a fire hazard.

- Keep outside tree branches away from the chimney. Keep the roof clean of leaves and other debris. Consider covering the chimney with a mesh spark arrester screen.

When removing ashes, place them in a covered metal container and set the container on a concrete or other noncombustible surface for several hours until cool. When thoroughly cooled, ashes can be thrown away with household trash. Cooled ashes also make good garden or flower fertilizer.

## Cooking

Simply whipping up breakfast can be a fire hazard. Be sure to follow these precautions in the kitchen.

Wear close-fitting clothing or an apron when you cook. Be careful to keep unfastened sleeves and other loose clothing away from the stove.

- Stay in the kitchen while you are cooking, and keep small children away from the stove.
- Turn cookware handles toward the back of the stove so hot pots and pans will not accidentally be bumped.
- Keep items that could easily catch fire, like pot holders and dishtowels, away from the stove.
- Wipe up all grease spills immediately.
- Put a lid on pan fires.
- If there is an oven fire, close the oven door and turn the oven off.

## Electrical Appliances

All electrical appliances should be operated according to the manufacturer's instructions. Exercise care when using anything that has to be plugged into an electrical supply.

- Unplug appliances when they are not in use. This is especially important for appliances such as toaster ovens, irons, and other appliances that get hot.

- Keep combustibles away from heat-producing appliances such as toasters and irons.

- Do not drape material over lamps. Use the correct bulb wattage for your lamp and shade; some lamp shades are flammable if used with bulbs brighter than 30 watts. Make sure lamps are secure and level, and that they will not easily fall over.

- Turn off halogen lamps whenever you leave a room because halogen bulbs get especially hot.

- Keep appliances in good repair, and make sure the electrical cords are not frayed or damaged.

- Keep electrical appliances away from water.

If an electrical appliance is plugged into an outlet and falls into water, **do not** reach into the water to retrieve it. The massive electrical shock the water would deliver could kill you.

"UNPLUG IT"
DO NOT REMOVE THIS TAG!
WARN CHILDREN OF THE RISK OF DEATH BY ELECTRIC SHOCK!

## Electrical Distribution Equipment

Extension cords and other wiring are essential to a modern home, but any use of electricity should be handled with care. Follow these precautions to stay safe.

- Always treat wiring as though it is on, "hot," or energized.
- Use the proper extension cord with the proper appliance. Use as few extension cords as possible, and do not overload them.
- Make sure extension cords are not under rugs or in any area where they might get worn down, stepped on, or damaged.
- Put plug covers on outlets if there are children around.
- Only plug appliances and other approved devices into an outlet.
- Keep ladders, especially metal ones, away from overhead wires. A ladder that touches an overhead wire can conduct massive amounts of electricity and electrocute anyone who touches it.

If an electrical outlet or switch feels warm, immediately shut off the circuit and call an electrician.

## Arson

Arson is the crime of purposely setting a fire for wrongdoing. About one in four fires in America is caused by arson. Arson is the second leading cause of death by fire. Only fires caused by smoking cause more residential-fire deaths. Arson is also the major cause of deaths, injuries, and dollar loss in commercial properties.

Arson is a felony that is punishable with a lengthy jail sentence. If the fire causes human injury, more time could be added to the arsonist's sentence. In most countries, if a fire set by an arsonist results in death, that arsonist is guilty of murder.

Most arsonists are under the age of 20. According to the U.S. Fire Administration, children start approximately 10,000 fires annually. In recent years, playing with fire has been the leading cause of fire deaths among preschoolers.

Some older kids start fires because they are bored or curious about fire. They do not respect or understand fire and the damage it can do. Professional firefighters know that fire is unpredictable and hard to control.

Other kids start fires because they are frustrated with some part of their lives. But fire is not the way to solve problems. In fact, arson can make a person's life much worse. These types of fire starters need counseling to address personal issues.

Here's what you can do to help prevent arson.

- Refuse anyone who tries to get you involved in setting a fire or experimenting with fire.

- Report anyone involved in fire play to your parents, counselor, fire department, or police department.

- Report any suspicious activity around buildings. Firefighters are three times more likely to be injured fighting an abandoned-building fire than one in an occupied building.

- If you know a child who plays with fire, treat that situation as if the child were playing with guns: Report it immediately. Remember that children as young as 2 are capable of setting fires.

## Seasonal and Holiday Fire Safety

Fires occur frequently during holidays and times of seasonal change. Following is a look at the major calendar-related fires and how they can be prevented.

### December–February

More fires occur during these cold winter months than during any other time of year. One reason is Christmas, Hanukkah, and New Year's holiday festivities. Especially important is the role of holiday decorations.

### TREES AND DECORATIONS

Artificial trees should be flame-resistant. Never string a metal tree with electric lights. Families who put up Christmas trees and who prefer natural trees to artificial trees should follow these guidelines.

- Be cautious about buying a tree that was cut weeks earlier. These trees will already be getting dangerously dry. Choose a tree whose needles do not fall off easily from its branches—shake it to see. If you buy a natural tree, try to get one locally, and cut it a few days before Christmas so that it does not dry out too much.

- At home, place the tree away from *all* sources of heat—at least 3 feet from heaters, fireplaces, furnaces—and make sure it does not block an exit. See that your tree is stable and will not tip over and harm someone, or fall in such a way that it could catch fire. Tie the tree with a nylon cord to the wall or ceiling for extra support.

- Cut the base of the natural tree at a 45-degree angle and place the trunk in water. Make sure that there is always water in the tree stand—some trees "drink" about a gallon a day.

- Inspect the tree daily, checking the electric lights and water in the base container. Shake the tree gently; if needles fall out, the tree has dried to the point it is dangerous and should be taken out.

**Buy and use only decorative electric lights with labels that indicate they have been listed by an approved testing facility like Underwriters Laboratories.**

- Use indoor lights on your tree, never outdoor lights. Inspect all light and electrical cords for fraying and other defects before use. Never leave lights turned on unattended; before going to bed or leaving the house, make sure all lights are turned off.

- After the holidays, promptly dispose of the tree, boxes, wrapping paper, and ribbon from your opened gifts. Never burn your tree, wrapping paper, boxes, or plastics in the fireplace or wood stove. These materials can give off toxic smoke; the evergreen materials burn extremely hot and can easily get out of control. Also, burning embers from these materials can float up the chimney, putting your home—and your neighborhood—in jeopardy.

Many people enjoy lighting candles during the winter holidays. Candles, like other sources of heat or flame, should never be used near a natural tree or around combustible decorations. Never put candles in windows. The candle flame, or the hot wax, could set wood, curtains, blinds, and carpeting on fire. Never put candles near exits. If a fire starts, your way out will be blocked. Never leave candles unattended. Leave the room or go to bed only after candles have been extinguished.

If you use a *menorah* (the special candleholder used in celebrating the Jewish festival of Hanukkah) or a *kinara* (the ceremonial candleholder used in the celebration of Kwanzaa), be sure to keep it away from drafty areas and combustible materials like curtains. Do not use paper to catch the hot wax that will fall from the candles. A large metal tray or other noncombustible material placed underneath the candleholder will prevent a candle from falling onto carpeting or some other combustible material.

Heating appliances are responsible for many fires that occur during the winter months. The safe use and handling of heating appliances is discussed in the chapter titled "Handling Fire Safely."

### FROZEN WATER PIPES

Use a hair dryer to safely thaw pipes. Using a blowtorch or other open-flame device to thaw pipes is careless and dangerous. The high heat from the flames will travel along the pipe and could ignite materials in the wall many feet away.

## March–May

Fire problems in spring shift outdoors. As the weather improves, we spend more time outside, especially cooking and camping. Outdoor fire safety is discussed in detail in the chapter titled "Fire Safety Outdoors."

Before spring rains trigger the growth of new plants, grass and brush from the previous season is highly flammable. Extreme care must be taken with open flames outside. Where possible, cut back or remove dead, fire-prone vegetation.

## June–August

Fireworks during the Fourth of July are a big fire hazard. In 1998, fireworks caused approximately 7,000 fires and 8,500 injuries in the United States. The safest way to handle fireworks is *not* to handle them. Leave fireworks to the professionals, and enjoy a public fireworks display at a park, ball field, or other outdoor venue.

Summer also triggers fire danger from outdoor cooking. Use portable grills and other outdoor cooking devices in an open area and never below an overhanging roof or in an unventilated space. Do not use portable grills on apartment decks if there is any potential of spreading dangerous fumes to the unit above or dropping hot coals to the unit below.

Be careful of any flame or heat source outdoors, including matches, cigarette butts, and sparks. If you see smoke outdoors that suggests a grass or brushfire, notify the fire department immediately.

## September–November

The fall months bring cool—even cold—weather to many parts of the country. This change in weather marks the return of heater-related hazards. Autumn is the time to clean and repair all heating appliances and to ready your home for winter.

October brings Halloween, another holiday demanding careful attention to fire danger. Two main fire hazards are associated with this time of the year. The first involves lit candles in jack-o'-lanterns. Use a flashlight instead. The other hazard is trick-or-treat costumes. Select those that are designated as flame-resistant or flame-retardant.

## Home Safety Inspection

Together with the other members of your family, use this checklist to check the safety of your house. Not every question will apply to your home. For each question that is answered with yes, score a point. When you are done, total your score. Where you have answered no, attempt to eliminate the hazards or change the actions. After a few days of making adjustments, review the list to see how much your score has improved.

Before burning autumn leaves, check with the fire department about local burn laws.

### FIRE SAFETY CHECKLIST

| Matches | Yes | No |
|---|---|---|
| Are matches kept where young children cannot reach them? | ☐ | ☐ |
| Are strike-anywhere matches kept in metal containers? | ☐ | ☐ |
| Are matches kept away from heat sources like stoves and heaters? | ☐ | ☐ |
| Are matches and smoking materials put out and cold before being discarded? | ☐ | ☐ |
| Do smokers use safety ashtrays? | ☐ | ☐ |
| Is "no smoking in bed" a house rule? | ☐ | ☐ |
| Does a responsible person watch the children when parents go out, even for a little while? | ☐ | ☐ |

Score _____

| Smoke Detectors | Yes | No |
|---|---|---|
| Are the smoke detectors in your home installed properly? | ☐ | ☐ |
| Are smoke detectors located in all sleeping areas of your home and on every level? | ☐ | ☐ |
| Are smoke detectors tested at least once a month? | ☐ | ☐ |

| | Yes | No |
|---|---|---|
| When the smoke detector sounds, does everyone know to get out of the house immediately? | ☐ | ☐ |
| If a smoke detector fails to operate when tested, is it fixed immediately? | ☐ | ☐ |
| Do you change the batteries in your smoke alarms at least once a year, on a birthday or holiday, or when you set your set your clocks forward in the spring or back in the fall? | ☐ | ☐ |
| Are your smoke detectors less than 10 years old? | ☐ | ☐ |

Score _____

**Electrical Hazards**

| | Yes | No |
|---|---|---|
| Are only qualified electricians allowed to install or extend wiring in your home? | ☐ | ☐ |
| When you buy electrical equipment—extension cords, appliances, televisions, and all other devices—do you always make sure it has been tested at an approved facility like Underwriters Laboratories? | ☐ | ☐ |
| Are there enough electrical outlets in each room to avoid the need for multiple attachment plugs and long extension cords? | ☐ | ☐ |
| Are there special circuits for heavy-duty appliances like stoves, air conditioners, and clothes dryers? | ☐ | ☐ |
| On the household-lighting circuit, are the proper fuses or circuit-breakers used? | ☐ | ☐ |
| Are all extension cords in the open—not run under rugs, over hooks, or through partitions or door openings? | ☐ | ☐ |

Score _____

**Storage and Flammable Liquids**

| | Yes | No |
|---|---|---|
| Are your basement, closets, balcony, and attic kept free of rubbish, oily rags, flammable liquids, and large stacks of paper, and is necessary storage kept in an orderly fashion? | ☐ | ☐ |
| After oily polishing rags are used, are they destroyed or placed in covered metal cans in a metal cabinet in the garage? | ☐ | ☐ |

| | Yes | No |
|---|---|---|
| If you store paint, varnish, or other flammable liquids, are the containers metal, tightly closed, and kept in a metal cabinet in the garage? | ☐ | ☐ |
| If you keep gasoline for use in a power mower or outboard motor, is it stored in an approved metal can with a self-closing cap on the openings? | ☐ | ☐ |
| If you burn coal, are ashes put in metal containers, clear of wood floors or partitions? | ☐ | ☐ |
| Has everyone in the family been warned never to use gasoline, benzene, or other flammable liquids to clean clothes, furnishings, or floors? | ☐ | ☐ |
| If your garage is attached to the house or in the basement, is it separated from the living area by cutoff walls with a tight-fitting door? | ☐ | ☐ |

Score _____

## Heating and Cooking

| | Yes | No |
|---|---|---|
| If you use oil heat, is the equipment listed by Underwriters Laboratories? | ☐ | ☐ |
| If you use gas heat, is the equipment listed by Underwriters Laboratories or the American Gas Association Laboratories? | ☐ | ☐ |
| If your heating system is oil or coal, do you have it inspected and serviced before each season begins? | ☐ | ☐ |
| If your heating system is gas, is it regularly checked and serviced? | ☐ | ☐ |
| Are all chimneys, gas and smoke pipes, and other flue connections inspected each fall and cleaned and repaired as necessary? | ☐ | ☐ |
| Are walls, ceilings, and partitions near heating and cooking equipment either adequately separated from the sources of heat or protected by noncombustible materials? | ☐ | ☐ |
| Are wood floors under space heaters or coal stoves protected by insulation or ventilated air space? | ☐ | ☐ |
| Is the inside basement door at the head of the stairs tightly fitted and kept closed at night? | ☐ | ☐ |

| | Yes | No |
|---|---|---|
| Is the kitchen stove, including the oven and broiler, kept clean of grease? | ☐ | ☐ |
| Is the kitchen exhaust fan kept clean of grease? | ☐ | ☐ |
| Are curtains arranged so they do not blow over stoves and heaters? | ☐ | ☐ |
| Are oil and gas heaters always turned off before everyone goes to bed? | ☐ | ☐ |
| Do all portable and space heaters sit level and out of the way of traffic? | ☐ | ☐ |
| Are oil and gas heaters, which use up oxygen as they burn, properly vented? Do you always keep a door or window slightly open in any room where such a heater is being used? | ☐ | ☐ |
| Are the fuel tanks of oil heaters refilled only by adults outdoors and in daylight? | ☐ | ☐ |
| Are the gas connections for space heaters or other gas appliances made of metal? | ☐ | ☐ |
| Has everyone in the family been warned never to use kerosene or other flammable liquids to start a fire in the fireplace or furnace? | ☐ | ☐ |
| Is every indoor fireplace equipped with a sturdy metal fire screen? | ☐ | ☐ |
| Are the shutoff valves for gas appliances located on the rigid metal gas pipeline where they can be reached in case of trouble without touching the appliance? | ☐ | ☐ |
| Have all electric, oil, or gas heaters been tested and listed by a recognized testing laboratory like Underwriters Laboratories? | ☐ | ☐ |

**Score** _____

| **Yard Hazards** | **Yes** | **No** |
|---|---|---|
| Do you keep your yard cleared of leaves, debris, and combustible rubbish? | ☐ | ☐ |
| In areas where burning trash is permitted, are trash and refuse burned only in suitable outdoor incinerators and on sufficiently calm days? | ☐ | ☐ |

| | Yes | No |
|---|---|---|
| Is an adult always present when trash or leaves are being burned outdoors? | ☐ | ☐ |
| Are charcoal grills used only outdoors and lit without the use of liquid fuels? | ☐ | ☐ |

Score _____

**Holiday Hazards**

| | Yes | No |
|---|---|---|
| Do you have a safe Fourth of July celebration by not using fireworks? | ☐ | ☐ |
| In buying gift toys, do you insist on those that can't cause fire, shock, or explosion? | ☐ | ☐ |
| Is the Christmas tree kept outside until you are ready to set it up? | ☐ | ☐ |
| Is the tree kept in water and thrown out when the needles begin to fall? | ☐ | ☐ |
| Is there a switch away from the tree for turning the lights on and off? | ☐ | ☐ |
| Are tree lights shut off whenever you go out or to bed? | ☐ | ☐ |
| Is all decorative lighting checked for frayed and loose sockets? | ☐ | ☐ |
| Are all decorating materials noncombustible? | ☐ | ☐ |
| Are candles placed so they cannot reach combustible materials? | ☐ | ☐ |
| Are gift wrappings gathered up and disposed of promptly after presents are opened? | ☐ | ☐ |

Score _____

**A Prepared Family**

| | Yes | No |
|---|---|---|
| Does every family member know the proper procedure for reporting a fire in your community, including 9-1-1 or other emergency telephone number, and the location of the neighborhood fire-alarm box? | ☐ | ☐ |
| Does every family member know how to call the fire department? | ☐ | ☐ |
| Are baby-sitters instructed carefully on what to do in case of fire? | ☐ | ☐ |
| Did the entire family take part in completing this checklist? | ☐ | ☐ |

Score _____

## Home Fire-Escape Planning

The actions taken during the first few minutes after a fire is discovered can be critical in determining whether the people involved will be survivors or victims.

Preparation is important to escaping a fire. In the case of an actual fire, you will not have much time to stop and think, so your actions for escape should be automatic, well-practiced, and routine.

Develop a plan to get everyone out of the house before you call the fire department. Because all family members need to know what to do in a fire, all should be involved in escape planning. The three steps in escape planning are planning, practice, and evaluation.

### Planning

To begin planning, sketch a floor plan of your house or apartment. Include all of the doors and windows, as well as what is under the outside windows. Label each room. Now you are ready to decide on the primary and secondary exits. *Primary exits* are those that you would normally use, like doors and hallways. Using a pen or pencil, draw a solid line from each room to the nearest outside door. The line should follow the hallways and routes that are the most direct to the exit. When these lines have been drawn, you have marked the primary exits.

DOWNSTAIRS

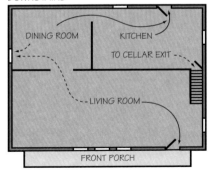

UPSTAIRS

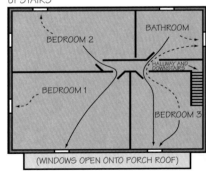

MAIN ROUTE ⟶    ALTERNATE ROUTE ----▸

Now you need to decide on the *secondary exits*. Go back to the starting point for each of the lines. Now draw a line to the nearest opening that goes directly to the outside. You probably will have to use some windows, but that is fine. These are the secondary exits. Of course, you now face some difficult problems.

If your house is all one floor at ground level, going out of a window might not be difficult, although sometimes windows are placed high in a wall and can be hard to reach from the inside. However, if you have rooms on a second or third floor, or if you live in an apartment building and are on an upper level, going out a window can be a problem. Also, things outside of the window, such as flower boxes, roof overhangs, and bushes can require special planning.

Because you cannot be sure that the primary exits will always be available in a fire, you must be able to use secondary routes. This could mean that you will have to plan to use an escape ladder from an upper-story window, or you might be able to climb out onto a roof and then down to the ground, or perhaps you will have to take shelter from the fire in the room and wait for firefighters to rescue you.

Some people will not be able to use a window exit safely, including elderly people, infants and small children, people with physical disabilities, and those above the third floor. If the primary exits are unavailable, and the person cannot use a secondary exit, that person should then *take shelter.*

After charting all of your exit routes, you must decide on a *meeting place.* This should be near the road, but not in it. Pick something to serve as a landmark, like a tree. Also choose a place from which to call the fire department. It is not a good idea to use the phone in the house (unless you are sheltering in a room with a phone), because you should get out quickly. Plan to use the neighbors' phone even if you have to wake them up, or to use a nearby pay phone (many do not need coins for emergency calls) or an alarm box.

Escape ladders stored beneath upper-story windows provide a secondary exit from bedrooms.

If it is necessary for you to take shelter in a room, remember to

- Close doors between you and the fire.

- Plug up air vents and cracks around the door to keep out smoke.

- Open the window for fresh air.

- Call the fire department if you have access to a phone.

- Signal from the window with something big, like a bedsheet.

- Calmly breathe the air close to the floor (heat and smoke rise) or from the open window.

When you have finished outlining the primary and secondary exits, the meeting spot, and the calling place, your plan is nearly complete. The only thing left to decide is when you are going to practice the plan.

## Practice

To be effective, *practices* should be held regularly. For most homes, once every two or three months should be enough practice after you have tested the plan. Here's a sample of one family's practice plan. Note that there are dates, times, and problems listed for each practice. All the family members know when the drill will take place so that they can review their actions.

Practice means having a fire drill. For the first part of the drill, have everyone go to his or her bedroom and pretend to be asleep. Then have someone set off the smoke alarm or yell, "Fire!" These are the signals for everyone to get moving. Get down on your hands and knees and crawl as if there were smoke or a fire.

## FIRE DRILL PRACTICE PLAN

| ESCAPE TIME | DATE | TIME | PROBLEM |
|---|---|---|---|
| 3 MIN. | JUNE 5 | 10 PM | Sleeping-Smoke detector alarms. All go out first exit. |
| 5 MIN. | JUNE 30 | 10AM | Everyone in bedrooms. Smoke detector alarms. All use window to exit. |
| _____ | JULY 10 | 7PM | Fire in the kitchen. Use nearest exit. |
| _____ | AUG 4 | 10PM | Sitter holds drill. |

Smoke and heat rise, so stay close to the floor in the event of a fire.

Another member of the family should time the drill from when the alarm sounds until everyone has arrived at the meeting spot. For the first fire drill, everyone should use the primary exits. After recording the time, go back into the house for the second part of the drill—using the secondary exits. Again, after that evacuation of your house or apartment, record the time. Your family probably will take a little longer to get out of your home because the exit routes are so different and can be a bit more difficult to use.

## Evaluation

After running the drill using primary and secondary exits, you are ready to *evaluate* your plan. Check with everyone after the second part of the drill to see if they encountered any problems using the secondary exits. If some part of your escape plan did not work well, implement and test other methods until the escape plan runs without problems. When everything seems to be working well, you have completed all three steps: planning, practice, and evaluation.

Now, pencil in drill dates on the family calendar and continue to practice on schedule. With regular practice, the actions that can help to save your family in a fire will become automatic. Continue to record the drill times on the chart to help uncover any problems that might have developed. Keep your plan flexible and be creative in solving the problems encountered in the drills.

If you live in an apartment, learn the fire escape plan for your building. Do not block exits that other people may need to use, like stairway exits and fire exits. Do not use the elevators. Consider getting a collapsible fire-escape ladder to use from the second floor. Do not put too many things on your balcony and thereby cause a fire hazard and fire-escape blockage.

Away from home, you must also have an escape plan. When staying with a friend or relative, or in a hotel, answer the following questions: Is there a fire alarm system? Are there smoke detectors or sprinklers? Where are the exits? Is there a window exit? Remember, elevators must not be used as exits during a fire.

## Smoke Detectors

The smoke detector or smoke alarm is the single most important piece of fire survival equipment in your home. Most fatal residential fires occur at night when people are asleep. Fires give off deadly gases, such as carbon monoxide, that can put people into a deep sleep or weaken their judgment. Smoke detectors are designed to alert you in the earliest stages of a fire, giving you and your family time to escape.

Smoke detectors are activated by smoke particles that are produced when a fire burns. Some of these particles are too small to see with the human eye, but a smoke detector can sense them. That explains why a smoke detector placed in the kitchen might go off when someone is cooking, even though there is no visible smoke.

**As an additional safety feature, many homeowners now install carbon monoxide detectors. These are available at most home improvement retailers.**

# Automatic Fire Signaling Systems

*Automatic fire signaling systems* are used by many hospitals, nursing homes, and other high-hazard occupancies. This fire-detection equipment automatically signals the fire department of an emergency. In fire-dispatch headquarters, a panel will light up and sound, indicating trouble at a particular location.

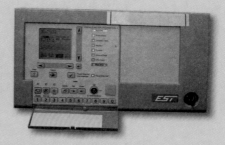

In a *central-station system*, rather than the fire department being notified directly when a detection device goes off, a signal sounds in the office of an independent agency, which normally is staffed 24 hours a day. The firm's personnel investigate these alarms and notify the fire department if there is an emergency.

A *local system* is the type found in most schools. The signal is heard only within the protected building. A local system is designed for the warning of occupants only.

## INSTALLING SMOKE DETECTORS

At least one smoke detector should be installed on every level of the home, including one in the basement. Modern building codes require that a smoke detector be put outside every bedroom.

The smoke detector should be mounted on the ceiling or high on the wall. Avoid putting the detector into dead air spaces; you want natural airflow to go past the detector. Do not mount a detector in a high corner where two walls and the ceiling meet. Also, avoid mounting a smoke detector near a central air-conditioning/heating register, which could push smoke away from the detector.

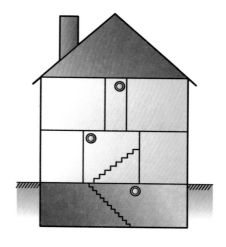

## TESTING AND MAINTENANCE

When the TV stops working, you know right away. How do you know if the smoke detector is in working order? Smoke detectors are made to be reliable, but some testing and maintenance is required.

Smoke detectors are electrical appliances that can be wired to the home's electrical system, be plugged into a wall outlet, or be battery-operated. Read and follow the manufacturer's instructions. To maintain your smoke detector:

- Test a battery-operated detector once a week, or once a month if connected to the electrical current. Most smoke detectors have a test button that will activate the alarm when pressed.

- Vacuum the detector once a month to help keep dust from interfering with operations.

- Change the batteries at least once a year—when you reset your clocks in the spring or fall, or an important date like a holiday or birthday.

- Track your smoke detector's age and replace old ones. The average life span of a smoke detector is 10 years.

Do not burn a candle under a smoke detector to test it; doing so might cause the monitor to fail in an emergency.

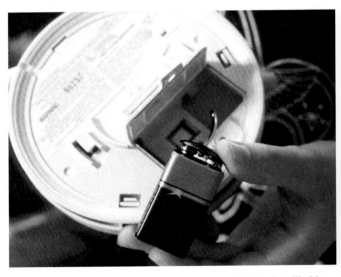

**If you forget to change a smoke detector's batteries, it will chirp or beep as it loses power. Change the batteries immediately.**

# Reporting a Fire Alarm

To report a fire in your home to the fire department, go to the nearest neighbor or outside phone. If the fire is outside your home, you can call from your home phone. Some communities and neighborhoods still use street fire-alarm boxes for emergencies, but chances are you will be using a telephone to report a fire or other emergency.

Learn the proper procedure for reporting a fire or emergency in your community. You might live in an area where you need only to dial 9-1-1 to reach emergency personnel. Other areas have different emergency numbers. If you are not sure what the emergency telephone number is, look inside the front cover of your phone book. Learn your fire department's telephone number as well. As a last resort, you can call the telephone operator. Do not wait until a fire or other emergency occurs to learn the proper procedure to follow.

If you call the fire department directly, the dispatcher will ask you for your name, the address of the fire or some other description of its location, and additional pertinent information. Stay on the line until the dispatcher tells you to hang up.

If you think there is a fire, call the fire department immediately. Do not stop to investigate. A delay of even a minute can make the difference between saving and losing a home—or a life.

Because the availability of water can be unpredictable in rural and remote areas, fire departments use water ponds to store water in such areas. These large contraptions look just like an above-ground pool—but they aren't made for swimming.

If you live in an area where street fire-alarm boxes are used, before an emergency occurs, learn the location of these boxes and how they work. You might want to visit the fire station nearest you and ask the firefighters how the alarm boxes work. If you report a fire or other emergency from a street fire-alarm box, stay at the street box location until the fire department arrives. A street fire-alarm box only tells where the alarm has been activated— not the location of the fire or emergency. You or someone else should be at that fire-alarm box location to direct firefighters to the site of the fire or emergency.

If you are in a public building, theater, or restaurant when you discover a fire, do not create confusion or panic by shouting. Tell the management or another adult that you think there is a fire. Pull a fire-alarm box in the building if one is available and then leave immediately.

In rural areas, forest fires and grass or range fires should be reported immediately to the fire department or the local forest service ranger.

Whenever you are in a public place, note where the exit signs are located so that you will be prepared in case of an emergency.

### False Alarms

No discussion of reporting a fire alarm would be complete without considering the irresponsible practice of deliberately reporting a false alarm. Firefighters risk their lives driving through traffic to respond to an alarm. If you report a false alarm, you are disobeying part of your Scout Oath—to help other people at all times. You also are breaking the law and could be arrested.

Firefighters on a false-alarm call might be unable to return quickly for an actual fire. Lives and property elsewhere could be lost needlessly. Never turn in a false alarm.

## Fire Extinguishers

Fire extinguishers have positive and negative aspects. On the positive side, a fire extinguisher used properly can prevent a small fire from getting out of control. On the negative side, a fire extinguisher might give you false confidence or a feeling that fire is not a danger because an extinguisher is available to put it out. People often waste valuable time fighting a fire with an extinguisher before sounding the alarm.

Fire extinguishers can be beneficial if they are controlled by someone who knows how and when to use them. Know where the fire extinguishers are located, and practice using them correctly. The moment you face a fire, regardless of its size, is not the time to learn how to use the extinguisher. Using a fire extinguisher calls for quick, sensible judgment. A contained fire, like one in a wastebasket or trash barrel, might easily be put out with an extinguisher. A blazing sofa might not. Do not waste valuable time using an extinguisher on a fire that is simply too large to put out. Instead, sound the alarm and get out.

## Classes of Fire and Fire Extinguishers

There are four classes of fire, each named by a letter of the alphabet. Extinguishers have been developed to work well on one or more of them. An extinguisher should say on its side, in words or pictures, the classes of fire that it can fight:

- *Class A fires* involve combustible materials like paper, wood, fabrics, rubber, and plastics. These fires can be squelched with water or insulated with tri-class (ABC) chemical or foam extinguishers.

- *Class B fires* involve gasoline, oil, grease, tars, paints, lacquers, or flammable gases. The oxygen that supports this type of fire must be cut off by tri-class (ABC), regular dry chemical, foam, or carbon dioxide extinguishers. Water is dangerous, as it spreads this type of fire.

Remember, a fire extinguisher is only a first-aid appliance. If the fire is serious enough to require a fire extinguisher, it is serious enough to sound the alarm and call the fire department first.

**Ordinary Combustibles**

**Water fire extinguishers are meant for use only on class A fires.**

**Flammable Liquids**

**A dry chemical fire extinguisher would be one choice to extinguish a class B fire.**

An alternative to using an extinguisher on an electrical fire is to unplug the cord or appliance, if this can be done safely. Water can then be used to extinguish the fire.

A class-B fire extinguisher is effective on a grease fire, but your first response should be to smother it with a lid. That way, you will avoid any risk of scattering the fire.

- *Class C fires* are electrical fires involving heated wiring, cords, and appliances. These fires must be suppressed with tri-class (ABC), dry chemical, or carbon dioxide extinguishers. Never use water, which transmits electricity and could lead to electric shock.

- *Class D fires* are a problem for industries that use or transport combustible metals like magnesium, sodium, potassium, uranium, plutonium, calcium, lithium, and titanium. They are extinguished by special powder extinguishers that rob the fire of oxygen and dissipate heat. Do not use a class D extinguisher on any other type of fire— it can be dangerous.

**D**

**Combustible Metals**

Fortunately, manufacturers have found ways of combining the compounds in extinguishers so that one extinguisher is capable of handling more than one class of fire. The rating for extinguishers includes a letter or letters indicating the class of fire, and a number indicating the extinguishing capability of the extinguishers.

A 20BC rating on an extinguisher means that it should be used only on flammable-liquid (class B) or electrical (class C) fires. The 20 means that this type of extinguisher can extinguish a fire twice as large as can an extinguisher rated 10BC.

**Electrical Equipment**

**A carbon dioxide extinguisher would be a good choice for a class C fire.**

**Class K extinguishers smother cooking fires.**

## Using Fire Extinguishers

A small fire is discovered in a wastebasket. An extinguisher rated for class A fires is nearby. What do you do? First, sound the alarm. Tell residents that there is a fire so that they can safely leave. It is easier to escape a small fire than a fire that has grown out of control.

Next, call the fire department. If you think you will feel ridiculous if they arrive after you have put the fire out, just think how you would you feel if you did not call and then failed to extinguish the fire.

Extinguishers should be mounted at shoulder level near a doorway. Extinguishers can lose pressure— and their effectiveness in an emergency—so they must be checked periodically. All extinguishers have a maintenance schedule attached to them; check this schedule and adhere to it. Perform a monthly visual check of the extinguisher's gauge to ensure the tank is full and the pressure is normal. At the same time, ensure that the extinguisher can be easily removed from the bracket and has no visible damage. If you find anything out of the ordinary, have the extinguisher professionally serviced.

Lastly, grab the extinguisher and make sure that you are between the fire and an exit. If the fire can't be controlled, you need a quick way out. Following the PASS system, extinguish the fire. If you have practiced using an extinguisher, it will not feel unfamiliar.

While you wait for the fire department to arrive, keep an eye on the fire in case it restarts. Be prepared to use the extinguisher again if this happens.

The National Fire Protection Association recommends the word *PASS* as a way to remember how to properly use an extinguisher.

**P**  *Pull* the pin or release the lock latch. Extinguishers are not all the same; practice with yours to ensure you can engage it.

**A**  *Aim* the extinguisher nozzle, hose, or horn.

**S**  *Squeeze* or press the handle.

**S**  *Sweep* from side to side at the base of the fire.

### Extinguishing Systems

Public buildings, manufacturing, and other industrial facilities can be protected with many different types of fire-extinguishing systems. A common system is the *hood extinguishing system* found in many restaurant cooking areas. Systems may use any of several extinguishing agents, including water, foam, carbon dioxide, halogen, or dry chemicals.

One system that is increasing in use is the *residential sprinkler system,* in which a sprinkler system automatically puts water on a fire through sprinkler heads. The water is fed to the sprinklers through pipes, usually suspended from the ceiling. Until recently, sprinkler systems were found almost exclusively in businesses and industry. Sprinkler companies are now producing systems designed for home use.

## If You Smell Smoke

If you are in a building and smell smoke, do not stop to gather your belongings. Alert friends and family members so everyone can evacuate the premises. Feel a door with the back of your hand. If the door is warm, do not go out that way— the hot smoke and/or flames on the other side of the door can harm you. Stay low to the ground as you are leaving to avoid inhaling smoke. You might have to crawl. Meet family members at the agreed-upon meeting place. Call 9-1-1 from a safe place or a call box.

## If You Smell Natural Gas

Natural gas is extremely combustible. It can ignite and explode merely from the spark of a light bulb being turned on or off. In its pure form, natural gas is odorless and colorless. It is treated with a distinctive smell—a little like rotten eggs—so that a leak can be detected more easily. A gas leak needs to be treated seriously.

If you smell a faint gas odor, first check if gas appliances (such as the burners on a gas stove) are turned off. Then, open doors and windows to let in fresh air and allow gas to escape. When the gas smell diminishes, have an adult check whether the pilot lights of appliances (water heater, furnace, oven) are lit. If you cannot determine the source of the leak, call a professional.

If the gas smell is strong, do not do anything that could cause the gas in the air to ignite, including lighting a cigarette, making a telephone call, turning a light on or off, or even using a flashlight. Extinguish any candles or other flames. Get yourself and your family out of the house quickly and call the gas company to report the emergency.

If you smell smoke in a public place, do not yell "fire." Quickly locate a manager or other adult and tell that person you smell smoke. Then leave the building.

# Burns

Burns are serious injuries that can have a dramatic effect on the human body. Because burns can easily cover large areas and penetrate the outer skin layers that protect us from infections, their effect can be far-reaching.

When a burn occurs, it is important to control the amount of damage as quickly as possible. Young children and elderly people are affected more seriously by burns and should seek medical help for any burn other than a minor, first-degree burn.

## Scalds

Scalds from hot liquids or steam are the most common kind of burns. Here are some ways to prevent scalds:

- Turn pan handles toward the back of the stove.
- For a shower or bath, first turn on cold water and then add hot water.
- Help young children adjust the water temperature when they are washing their hands.
- Set the water heater's thermostat to 120 degrees.
- Keep hot liquids like soup and coffee away from children.
- Never use a wet oven mitt or towel to handle something hot. The water can turn to steam and burn you. Steam is hotter than boiling water.

The first step in controlling the damage done by a scald is to remove the heat. When soup or hot coffee is spilled, it might run off the skin, but it will soak into fabrics that will keep burning the skin. Take them off and immediately apply cool water to the burned areas to reduce the heat and lessen the degree of burn.

## Flame Burns

Flame burns from clothes that are on fire are the second most common kind of burns. The quickest way to extinguish a fire like this is to *stop* where you are, *drop* to the ground, and *roll* out the fire. Roll over and back, covering your face with your hands until the flames are completely smothered.

After the fire is out, rinse the area with water for 10-15 minutes to help *cool* the skin and reduce the damage.

The same technique should be used if someone else's clothes catch fire: Stop, drop, roll, and cool. If necessary, tackle the person to get him or her to the ground. A blanket thrown around the person will help smother the flames.

After cooling the burn, examine the injuries. (If clothing is sticking to the person's body, do not try to peel it off.) If the burn is small, cover it with a clean, dry cloth and seek medical attention. If the burn covers a large area, such as an entire arm or leg, or much of the chest or back, get the burn victim to professional medical aid immediately.

The National Fire Protection Association reports that when a fire occurs in a building with sprinklers, fewer people are burned and less property is damaged.

# Handling Fire Safely

A tiny match can spark a forest fire that destroys hundreds of acres of Earth's beauty. People who handle fire should always keep safety at the forefront, and the best way to do that is to follow some basic safety techniques.

## Matches

Matches are a convenient tool—we use them routinely to light the fireplace, birthday candles, campfires, and many other necessary fires. If they are used improperly, though, people can get hurt and property can be destroyed. Knowing the correct way to light and handle matches is an essential skill.

Children are curious and do not understand the dangers of matches and lighters. Always keep matches and lighters out of their reach.

Here is the proper procedure for lighting a match:

- Remove one match from its container and close the container. **Note:** Strike-anywhere matches are dangerous and must not be used.

- Hold the match firmly, away from your head, and identify what you want to light.

- Make sure no one is in front of you, then strike the match by drawing it quickly across the grainy striking surface. Try to strike the match with a motion going away from your body, not toward you.

- Light the object, and then extinguish the match.

- Dispose of the match in an ashtray, or hold it until it is cold.

## Charcoal Fires

Any open flame must be handled with care. A Scout might have frequent contact with the flame from a charcoal cooking fire. A number of safety precautions must be followed to avoid having an unfriendly fire.

The widespread use of charcoal lighter-fluids requires us to use these fluids with the greatest degree of safety. Before using a charcoal lighter fluid, read all directions thoroughly. Make certain that you are using an approved fluid for outdoor cooking—not kerosene, gasoline, or some other dangerous flammable liquid.

Heap the charcoal into a pyramid and apply the recommended amount of fluid. Then close the cover of the fluid can and set it down away from the charcoal. Next, light the match and apply it to the coals. Be careful to extend your arm fully and to keep your body as far away from the charcoal as possible. Never lean over the charcoal during lighting.

Whenever you are trying to ignite charcoal, make sure that all children are well away from the area. Use charcoal only on level ground and only in a stable cooker that will not tip over.

People who live in apartments, townhouses, or two-story homes must avoid using charcoal beneath a balcony or overhang. The flames from the burning charcoal can sometimes reach high enough to endanger the building construction above them.

**Whenever you are around an open flame, wear tight-fitting clothes to reduce the chances of their catching fire.**

Charcoal is not meant for use inside the home. Many people make the dangerous error of using charcoal grills for cooking or heating in enclosed areas such as garages, basements, porches, cabins, tents, or automobiles.

People have been overcome by carbon monoxide after taking a burning grill into an enclosed area during rainy or cool weather. Even putting the grill into a fireplace is dangerous. Only homes that have a special indoor barbecue pit with a vent to carry away carbon monoxide fumes are safe.

Campers have been suffocated while trying to heat cabins and tents with charcoal briquettes. It is not true that charcoal is safe when all surfaces of the briquette have become coated with gray ash. As long as the fuel is giving off heat, it is burning and dangerous in any unventilated area.

You can make an excellent charcoal fire-starter from a big metal can, like a large coffee can. Before removing the bottom, take a beverage can opener and punch a row of triangular holes around the base of the can, about an inch apart. Remove both the top and bottom of the can. You will have a cylindrical chimney open at both ends.

To use the fire-starter, place this chimney in the center of the charcoal grill and put two or three handfuls of crumpled and twisted paper in the bottom. Use waxed paper or milk cartons if possible. Pile charcoal briquettes on top of the paper until the can is filled. Light the paper through one of the triangular holes at the base, and the chimney will send hot flames roaring up through the briquettes. When you notice gray patches appearing on the topmost charcoal, use pliers or tongs (never your fingers) to lift the hot can straight upward. The burning charcoal will spread out in an even mound, ready for cooking.

Never store a charcoal grill next to the house. A number of recorded fires have been started spontaneously by charcoal that reignited long after the fire had been extinguished. Store charcoal in a dry place.

## Melting Wax

Hot wax is extremely flammable and can burst into flames without warning. Melting wax on a stove or campfire can be a hazardous procedure. Never try to melt wax in any sort of container directly on an open flame. Instead, boil water in a pan or kettle, keeping the water level low enough so that it will not overflow when another container is lowered into it. When the water is boiling, carefully remove it from the fire. Now lower the container of wax into the water slowly, holding it with pliers or tongs to avoid scalding yourself. The boiling water will soon melt the wax without exposing it to open flames.

## Pan Fires

Cooking fires are fairly common. They do not, however, need to become major fires or result in serious burns. The procedure for putting out a grease pan fire is simple, but it must be followed closely.

It is a good idea to have the necessary firefighting equipment (such as a class K extinguisher) handy before you begin to work. In this case, the equipment is a lid that will cover the entire pan. If the pan you are using does not have a lid, use a cookie sheet or another, larger pan. If the grease ignites, turn the heat off and slide the lid over the pan, covering it completely. Use a pot holder or oven mitt to lessen the danger of burning your hand. Also, tilt the bottom of the cover away from you for protection from the flames.

After waiting at least five minutes for the pan and grease to cool, you can carefully slide the cover off. Do not stand over the pan.

While most pan fires are small, the heat from the flames can ignite cabinets or walls around the stove. After smothering the fire in the pan, feel the cabinet and walls for heat. If they feel warm or if they appear to have darkened in color, call the fire department immediately.

## Heaters

Heater-related fires are the leading cause of residential fires in the United States. If your family uses auxiliary heaters, you should know the recommended clearance around them and how to fuel them properly.

### Kerosene Heaters

Use only an Underwriters Laboratories–listed heater that has a tip-over shutoff mechanism. Most kerosene heater manufacturers recommend using 1K kerosene fuel, which produces lower levels of toxic gases. Never use even a small amount of gasoline in a kerosene heater. Fuel the appliances outdoors, away from the house, on a level surface. Avoid overfilling and spilling. Store the kerosene in an approved metal container. Never fill a hot appliance; allow it to cool for a few minutes before refueling. Use the heater only in a well-ventilated room or area. Before you use this type of heater, check local fire codes or insurance companies' standards to be sure that your kerosene heater is approved for use.

### Wood-Burning Stoves

Have the stove checked by an expert before you use it. Read and follow the manufacturer's instructions on what type and amount of fuel to burn. Start the fire using paper and kindling; never use a flammable or combustible liquid of any kind in a wood stove and never use green wood. Artificial logs made of sawdust and wax, which are supposed to be burned one at a time, should not be put into a wood-burning stove. The stove's heat can melt the wax in the log instead of burning it, and this hot wax can leak out or flare up.

When adding wood to the stove, be sure to wear flame-resistant clothes and an oven mitt. Open the stove door slowly and carefully. Keep an extinguisher or a bucket of sand or water nearby.

## Coal-Burning Stoves

Do not overload a coal stove. Ignite the coal with paper and wood first. Because a coal stove can easily overheat, adjust the draft to control the rate of burning. Because coal stoves produce high levels of carbon monoxide, use them only in well-ventilated areas. These stoves generally do not require the frequent addition of fuel that wood stoves do.

## Fireplaces

Fireplaces also can be easily overfueled. Burn only one or two wood logs at a time. Carefully follow all of the manufacturer's directions for using artificial logs; they should be burned one at a time and not split apart or broken. Do not use a combustible or flammable liquid on the fire—the result is usually an explosive flash that can ignite a major fire.

Once a fire is started in the fireplace, close the screen or door securely. Make sure the fireplace has a mechanism to keep all embers safely within the firebox.

# Flammable Liquids

All substances are made up of molecules in motion. They move in different directions at various speeds. At higher temperatures, they move with more energy and more speed. If the molecules of a substance reach a high enough speed, they escape from the surface of the substance into the air. The molecules that remain in the air are called *vapor*.

Flammable liquids are different from other liquids because less heat is required for them to vaporize. These vapors are combustible under ordinary temperatures. Whenever a container of flammable liquid is open, vapors are escaping and a fire is possible.

When vapor escapes from a flammable liquid, it mixes with air. This vapor-air mixture provides two of the three necessary ingredients for fire: fuel and oxygen. All that is necessary for combustion to occur is the right amount of heat.

Without proper ventilation, vapor levels can quickly build up and become dangerous. Vapor is invisible. It can travel from floor to floor in a house and to an ignition source that is incorrectly considered a safe distance away. A dangerous concentration of vapor might be present without your knowledge.

In general, avoid working indoors with flammable liquids. If you are cleaning paintbrushes by soaking them in paint thinner or turpentine, for example, put them outdoors.

Sometimes it is necessary to use flammable liquids indoors, like certain cleaning products or adhesive removers. However, gasoline should never be used indoors. Gasoline vapor ignites more easily than any other flammable liquid vapor and should be used only as engine fuel.

## Proper Clothing for Working With Fire

Some materials burn more rapidly than others. Some materials drip as they burn, creating severe burns. Here are some basic facts to help you decide what to wear when you are building a campfire, fueling a boat motor, or cooking at home.

The materials used to make up fabrics fall into two broad categories: *natural* and *synthetic.* Natural materials include cotton and wool. Silk is the most flammable of the natural materials. Wool is the least flammable. Synthetic materials do not come from plants or animals, but are developed in laboratories and often are petroleum derivatives. Synthetic materials include polyester (also known as microfiber and synthetic fleece), acrylic, acetate, nylon, and rayon. Synthetic fabrics are slower to ignite than natural ones, but once they catch fire they melt and can cause serious burns. Some fabrics are a combination of natural and synthetic materials. You may have a T-shirt that is a blend of cotton and polyester fibers.

Synthetic and natural materials can be dipped or sprayed with substances that will inhibit their ability to ignite or continue burning. Some synthetic materials have this resistance built in. Fiberglass materials and special fire-resistant fabrics do not burn because their chemical makeup will not allow ignition. These materials, however, can be expensive and are not as adaptable as other fabrics.

Federal legislation regulates the flame resistance of children's sleepwear, mattresses, carpets, upholstery, and some camping equipment. These standards are used in burn tests conducted at various national laboratories.

*Weight* and *weave* also play a role in how a fabric burns. Heavier fabrics, especially those with tight weaves, burn more slowly than lightweight, open-weave fabrics. If you compare denim jeans to a T-shirt, you will notice that the fabric used in the jeans is heavier than what is used in the T-shirt. Both are made of cotton, but the denim has a heavier weave. When judging the weave's tightness, consider how much light you can see through the fabric. You probably can see some light through a T-shirt but not through denim. Nappy fabric, like an old, fluffy flannel shirt, will catch fire more readily than hard, smooth fabrics like canvas.

Be aware of the cut of the clothing you choose when you know you will be cooking, tending a fire, or working with fuel. For instance, you do not want to unintentionally drag an unbuttoned shirtsleeve across a flame or let your loose, long pant cuffs become soaked with gasoline. You do not want an oversized T-shirt to billow away from your body and touch a hot charcoal grill.

> Whenever you are near fire or flammable liquids, wear clothing that is styled in a fire-safe way.

When determining the relative flammability of fabrics, consider these factors:

- Weight—Heavier fabrics are less likely to burn.

- Weave—Dense fabrics are less likely to burn than more open fabrics.

- Construction—The smoother the surface, the less likely it is to burn.

- Style—Loose-fitting garments can ignite more easily than tight-fitting ones.

If the engine runs out of gasoline while being used, allow it to cool before refueling. Some of the parts could be hot enough to ignite any spilled fuel.

It is best to begin using a lawn mower with a full tank of gasoline.

## Fueling How-Tos

Gasoline-powered engines like those in lawn mowers and edgers need their fuel replaced from time to time, just like a campfire needs more wood to keep burning. To keep yourself safe and your equipment in good repair, follow these general safety precautions when fueling.

• Fill the engine's fuel tank outdoors, at least 6 feet from any building or structure.

• Position the engine firmly on level ground.

• From a standing position (do not kneel), using a pour spout or funnel, slowly pour gasoline (usually unleaded, unless the manufacturer's instructions call for another type, such as diesel) from an approved safety can into the engine's fuel tank, taking care not to overfill or spill the gasoline. Should any spills occur, thoroughly rinse the engine with lots of water. Do not wipe up the spill with a rag or cloth; wiping a spill simply produces another fire hazard in the form of vapors from a gasoline-soaked rag.

• Before starting the engine, replace the gasoline cap and allow any areas of spillage to dry. Be sure the gas can is secured several feet away from the engine when you start it.

• Keep children well away from the engine during fueling.

# Fire Safety Outdoors

Our forests are a national treasure to be enjoyed and protected.
Responsible camping practices and outdoor safety habits are
essential in preserving human and animal life, our environment,
and our natural resources.

Exercising extreme caution with campfires and brushfires
would reduce forest fires by about one-fifth. But an even simpler
precaution—careful use of matches and smoking materials—
would cut the loss by another 20 percent.

## Wildland Fires

Every year in the United States, forest fires destroy thousands
of acres of forest and timberland. Careless camping results in
burns, fire injuries, and deaths. People must learn and practice
fire-safe habits while enjoying the great outdoors.

### Types of Wildland Fires

Fires in the forest and field can be classified in many ways.
A *grass fire* usually involves a relatively small field of hay or
rye, and can become increasingly dangerous as it extends into
a wooded area or involve nearby houses, garages, and barns.
In the West, grass fires can cover hundreds of square acres.
Where the grass is high or where fire extends into a grain field,
fighting the blaze is a difficult and dangerous job.

*Surface fires* in the forest spread in the leaf litter and
underbrush. Less common, but more difficult to control, is the
*ground fire,* which burns deep below the surface in spongy leaf
litter and peat, eventually breaking to the surface.

Most dangerous and damaging of all is the *crown fire,*
which spreads quickly through the treetops. The period of
greatest danger is the spring or early fall when leaves are dry.

# The Cost of Fire

Death and personal injury are the overriding concerns of wildland fires. Wildland fires are also significant because they can damage buildings, timber crops, wildlife and their habitat, and soil. All of these losses are costly to humans.

The cost of putting out the fire, no matter how small, is significant. In most cases, the local fire department will extinguish it. In a department with paid firefighters, it costs money to send a crew and equipment to a fire. In a volunteer fire department, the costs include equipment as well as the lost work time of the volunteer firefighters.

Another firefighting cost is the damage caused by a serious fire that is unattended because fire units are extinguishing a woods fire. If a fire destroys a business, the chances are less than half that the business will reopen in the same location. Thus, the fire results in lost jobs, reduced tax revenues to the community, and increased social service expenses. The direct and indirect costs of woods fires affect us all.

# Camping Safety

All the fire safety principles suggested by the home fire-safety checklist apply to your camping home-away-from-home as well, particularly to a campsite with permanent buildings. Follow these specific camp-safety rules to keep yourself and fellow campers safe.

- Make sure to have some type of alarm that can be clearly heard throughout camp. If a fire breaks out, all campers should know in a matter of minutes. If organized fire protection is nearby, everyone in camp should know how to call it.

- Remove all flammable rubbish and leaves from around buildings and tents.

- Hang towels to dry away from stoves and heaters.

- Collect fireplace and stove ashes in covered metal containers to cool, then dispose of them properly.

- Make a nightly check of the camp before tucking in to see that all fires and lights are out or suitably protected.

## Campfires

During periods of forest-fire danger, it is sometimes necessary to get a permit before making a fire in national forests and similar areas. Observe these rules carefully.

Campfires should be built only in safe places, on sand or other mineral soil or rocks, and never next to trees. All flammable materials should be cleared away at least 10 feet around an outdoor fire, and the fire should never be left unattended. When an outdoor fire is put out, stay with it until the ashes are cool enough to handle with bare hands.

A campfire can become a danger unless it is kept small. A large fire with limbs and wood piled high will light up the entire circle, but sparks can be carried a considerable distance by a light wind or gust.

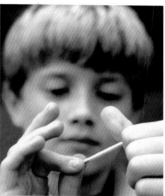

## Matches

Too often, a careless person discards a match in dry leaves or grass and causes a fire. To avoid starting a fire of this type, make sure matches are thoroughly extinguished before they are discarded. Shake or blow out a match to extinguish it. Before discarding the match, ensure that it is cool by rolling the tip of the match between your fingers.

Select a campfire spot with regard for wind and the surrounding area into which sparks will blow. Carefully clear the nearby ground of dead leaves, pine needles, and leaf mold down to the mineral soil and rake or sweep a 10-foot area around the base of the fire. Good, solid earth affords the only safe base. Avoid spongy, porous earth or peaty soil. Fire and heat can penetrate into the ground and travel under the surface, along fuses like roots, to crop up some distance away, causing *sleeper fires.*

During the life of a campfire, at least one of the group's older members should be appointed camp fire warden, with responsibility to see that the fire never gets out of control. This should be a continuous watch with adequate relief. The warden should have two or three pails of water placed near the fire, not to be used for any purpose other than fire control. To extinguish fires started by sparks, always have the pails filled. Gallon-size cans fixed with wire handles and filled with water should be at every tent.

When the time comes to break camp, a fire should be carefully put out and not left to burn out by itself.

## Camp Stoves and Lanterns

For generations, an open fire provided light at night and a means for most camp cooking. While it is still important to know how to kindle a blaze, many Scouts now prefer to carry lanterns and cook over lightweight stoves, practices that help protect the land and provide an added convenience.

Using a camp stove allows the flexibility of preparing meals quickly and neatly whether you are camping high above the tree line, in the deep snows of winter, or at the edge of an arid sandstone canyon. While a stove is a wonderful tool, it must be handled intelligently. Follow these guidelines when using a camp stove:

- Use camp stoves and their fuels only with adult supervision. Practice using them before your outing, carefully following the manufacturer's directions.

- Place stoves and charcoal grills on a level, secure surface, in ventilated areas only.

- Do not overload the stovetop with heavy pots or large frying pans. Keep pan lids handy to smother a grease fire if necessary.

- Keep fuel in well-marked, approved containers that are stored in a ventilated, locked box at least 20 feet from all buildings and tents. Store and refill fuel containers away from any flames.

- Never fuel a stove inside a cabin or tent; always do it outdoors.

- Allow a hot stove to cool before changing or refilling cylinders.

- Take home empty containers for proper disposal.

Follow these basic safety procedures for burning lanterns:

- Read and follow instructions.

- Keep the lantern in proper working condition.

- Only use lanterns outdoors.

Two basic types of lanterns are used in camping. Battery-operated, portable electrical lanterns are reliable and safe for both indoor and outdoor use. Fuel-burning lanterns use the same types of fuels as camp stoves, but instead of having an open flame, they contain a *mantel.* When ignited, the material glows and gives off a bright light.

## TYPES OF FUEL

*Butane* and *propane* are clean, highly combustible, pressurized gases stored in metal cylinders. Stoves using butane or propane are light, compact, and uncomplicated. Simply attach a cylinder, turn the regulator knob, and light the burner. You will have several hours of quiet, steady heat.

Because it has a high *flash point* (the temperature at which the gas bursts into flame), *kerosene* is among the safest and most readily available of stove fuels. A kerosene stove must be preheated by squeezing a dab of special flammable paste onto the base of the burner and touching a lighted match to it before igniting the burner itself. An air pump regulates the fuel tank pressure, and thus the height of the flame. Kerosene stoves can be a bit bulky, but they are reliable in any season.

*White gas* is highly refined, extremely flammable, and potentially explosive. Use it with the utmost caution. Some white-gas stoves have air pumps to provide the pressure necessary for ignition and an even flame, while others must be preheated. Follow the instructions for your stove exactly.

A variety of stoves use charcoal, canned flammable jelly, burnable pellets, or some other petroleum-based fuel. The stove you use should be designed for the job you expect it to do.

### CARRYING FUEL

The amount of fuel you will need depends on how much you plan to use your stove or lantern. You probably will need to take along more fuel than the stove or lantern can hold.

Butane and propane cylinders are ready to pack just as they are, but if you use kerosene or white gas, carry it only in a container made especially for that purpose. Buy a high-quality metal fuel bottle with a secure lid. Get one that is a different color than your water bottles to avoid confusion, and wrap several strips of tape around fuel bottles to help you correctly identify them in the dark.

Prevent gas fumes from spoiling your food by storing fuel bottles and cylinders in plastic bags, separate from food.

Remember that when a fuel is under pressure, its burning characteristics change. This usually means that the fuel is more dangerous and should be handled with extreme care.

# Managing and Putting Out a Fire

Build each fire just large enough for your needs. This will minimize the amount of wood you will burn and can make it easier to erase signs of a fire once you are done.

Extinguish every fire when you no longer need it or if you won't be around to watch it. Splash water on the embers, then stir the damp ashes with a stick and splash them again. Repeat this process until the fire is *cold out*—cold enough so that when you hold your hand just above the ashes, you do not feel any heat.

Sometimes you will build your fire in a permanent fire site. Clean such sites by picking out any bits of paper, foil, and unburned food. Pack them home with the rest of your trash. If you have made a new fire site, get rid of all evidence that it was ever there. Scatter any rocks, turning sides that have been blackened by soot toward the ground. Spread cold ashes over a wide area and toss away any unused firewood. Replace ground cover. When you're done, the site should look just as it did when you found it.

Take responsibility for every campfire by keeping an eye on it at all times.

### Breaking Camp

When cleaning up a campsite, similar precautions must be taken with burning brush and rubbish. Rubbish fires, like all campfires, should be constantly attended. If the fire gets out of control, it should be fought by adult leaders. Pails of water and implements like brooms, spades, and bundles of green boughs are useful in putting out a running brush or grass fire. If possible, burn all waste materials in metal containers or fireplaces that confine the fire. In any event, burn small piles at a time, feeding new material gradually.

# Matches and Fire Starters

Take along wooden matches for lighting your stove. Store them in a match safe or small plastic container with a tight lid. Some matches are commercially waterproofed; you can further protect regular matches by dipping them in melted paraffin. To be safe, keep some matches in your pocket and some with your fire starters.

Chances are you will not build an open fire in the backwoods, but in an emergency, if you must start a fire to get dry or to signal for help, you might need a fire starter. You can make them at home by tying a short length of rolled newspaper with string and dipping it in melted wax, or you can save candle stubs. Commercial fire starters come in tablet and paste forms. Keep all fire starters with matches in a sturdy plastic bag, and save them for use in an emergency.

# Careers in Fire Safety

Firefighters are people-oriented. They want to help others in need. This characteristic is the motivation behind volunteer fire departments and is one of the reasons why many firefighters are active in community affairs.

## Your Fire Department

The fire department has many roles. It fights and investigates fires and provides emergency medical services. It is the primary source of aid in an emergency like a building collapse or lost person, and natural disasters like tornadoes, floods, and snow-storms, and fire department employees also might monitor downed power lines so that people will not touch them. The fire department provides fire inspection and code enforcement to make sure buildings and operations are in compliance with state and local fire codes and ordinances. It also provides fire-safety education for the community.

Roughly 90 percent of the communities in the United States are served by volunteer fire departments. However, career fire departments provide protection to the greatest number of people. Generally, volunteer departments are found in rural areas; career departments are more common in urban areas.

Firefighters must be in excellent physical condition because fire-suppression activities demand that the firefighters work at maximum pace for long periods of time in extremely difficult conditions. Firefighters must leap into action at the sound of the alarm without the luxury of doing warm-up exercises. While firefighters are always subjected to heat in the fire area, in winter they also face bitter cold.

## Inspections and Prefire Planning

Firefighters inspect buildings for fire hazards. These inspections also allow the firefighter to study the building and to determine how a fire in that building should be fought. This is called *prefire planning.*

## Education

By working with teachers, nurses, and others who have contact with many people, the firefighter spreads the message of fire safety. Some fire departments establish public education divisions to provide this service.

Public fire educators design programs for preschools, elementary schools, junior and senior high schools, and businesses and industries. Public fire educators develop brochures and posters and even produce films that teach people how to prevent and survive fires.

Fire educators sponsor fire-safety demonstrations in shopping malls and other public places, often during National Fire Prevention Week each year during the week of October 9.

Often, a fire department's public education unit uses community volunteers to assist with lifesaving education programs. Interested Scouts should check with their local fire department to see how they can help.

## Code Enforcement

Specialized units of the fire department also provide fire-safety code enforcement and interpretation services. These units monitor the design and construction of buildings to make sure they incorporate fire-safety features.

One specialized fire truck is the *rescue truck,* which contains gas masks and inhalators, life nets, and medical equipment. It also carries equipment that firefighters use to rescue people from collapsed and caved-in buildings. *Hazardous materials trucks* contain special chemicals firefighters use on chemical spills. The people who work on these trucks have special training, clothing, and monitoring devices for dealing with hazardous materials. *Field communications trucks* contain sophisticated electronic equipment to help firefighters delegate tasks in emergency operations.

# Types of Fire Trucks

**Pumper truck**

**Tank truck**

**Ladder truck**

There are three main types of fire trucks and many kinds of specialty trucks. The main types are pumper, ladder, and tank trucks.

*Pumper trucks* are sent out on the first alarm. They carry hoses, water, and pumps to deliver water to the fire site. The pumper truck's equipment can help firefighters start cooling the fire right away, while other firefighters are attaching hoses to nearby fire hydrants. Some rural-area pumper trucks also have equipment to suction water from local ponds and rivers.

*Tank trucks* have a much bigger supply of water than pumper trucks. They are needed especially when fire hydrants are not available.

*Ladder trucks* carry long ladders and other equipment to help firefighters get up high to spray water, break windows, and cut holes in the roof of the structure to let out smoke and heat.

## Fire Department Survey

To gather additional important information about fire and fire safety, contact your local fire department or fire company. Ask to interview the officer on duty or the chief. Use the following questions when gathering information. Feel free to ask additional questions.

- Are the firefighters in this department career, volunteer, or a combination?

- How many people are in this department?

- How many people are at the station during a shift?

- How many fire alarms does the department answer in a year?

- What is the most frequent cause of residential fires in the department's territory?

- Who conducts the community's building inspections?

- Who does the fire investigations?

- Who teaches fire safety?

- What kind of training must a firefighter have?

- How old must a person be to become a firefighter?

- What types of emergency services does the fire department provide?

- How has fire fighting changed recently?

- What are some favorite pieces of firefighting equipment?

- How can the community help the fire department accomplish its goals?